Goblin Princess

nickelodeon
Winx CLUB

Fairy Colouring!
64

74 **Edible Necklace!**

Zoe

bursting with sparkly things for you. We have stories, puzzles, colouring, mazes, games and loads more with all your favourite friends, including Rainbow Magic, Littlest Pet Shop, My Little Pony, Polly Pocket, Strawberry Shortcake and more! Don't forget to log on to our website, www.mysparkleworld.com for chances to win prizes and lots more activities and fun!

Sparkly Kisses!

Sparkle World
xXx

www.mysparkleworld.com

Bingo Game!
38
Best Friends BINGO!

JEWELLERY BOX!
24

Puppy Maze!
62
PUPPIES IN PERIL!

12 **Spot the Difference!**
SPOT THE DIFFERENCE

···
···
Write your name here.

This super sparkly **Sparkle World** annual belongs to

Matilda the Hair Stylist Fairy!

1

Kirsty and Rachel were waiting at the hairdressers in a new shopping centre. All of a sudden, Matilda the Hair Stylist fairy appeared in front of the girls' mirror.

2

"Jack Frost's goblins have stolen my magical hairbrush!" said Matilda. "They're using it to turn everyone's hair blue! I have to get it back!" "We'll help you," promised Kirsty.

3

The two girls looked out of the window and noticed lots of people with blue hair. "Oh, no!" gasped Rachel, "The goblins have already started using the hairbrush!"

4

The girls spotted a sign saying 'Ice Blue Hair Salon'. Two goblins were writing down appointments. "We have to stop them before they turn more people's hair blue!" cried Kirsty.

"The magical hairbrush might be inside," said Rachel. "We have to get a closer look." "If I turn you into fairies we can get inside without being seen," said Matilda. She waved her wand and the girls shrank to fairy-size.

5

6

The three friends flew in to the salon and saw a goblin hair stylist, in his hand was the magical hairbrush. "Quick! There's the brush!" cried Matilda. "Fairies!" squealed the goblin. "Leave me alone!"

"Yowch!"

7

Rachel and Kirsty tried to grab the hairbrush before he could get away, but only managed to grab his long blue hair. "Yowch," squawked the goblin, as it slipped off. "It's a wig!" said a suprised Rachel.

8

With a jerk, he pulled it out of their hands and fell over. The wig flew through the air and landed in a rubbish bin with a loud SPLAT! The goblin grabbed the wig out of the bin and put it back on, sniffing sadly.

Suddenly, Rachel had an idea. "Matilda's magic can make your wig as good as new," she told the goblin. "All you have to do to make the magic work, is give her back her hairbrush!" The goblin handed it over to Matilda at once.

As soon as Matilda touched the magical hairbrush it shrank to fairy-size. Instantly the goblin's long blue hair was clean and silky again. The goblin gave a squeal of delight and began tying it up in bunches.

"We did it! We got the magical hairbrush off the goblin!" said Rachel. With a flick of the brush, Matilda reversed the blue hair spell for all of the goblin's customers. "Wow!" smiled Kirsty, "Everyone looks fabulous now!"

Matilda waved her wand to restore the girls to human size, and rewarded them with two sparkling hair clips. "They're beautiful," smiled Rachel. "Thank you!" It was a wonderful end to a magical day!

Strawberry Shortcake™

What's your Perfect Princess Name?

Sparkle World PUZZLE

Using your initials and the list below, find out your perfect princess name! You can also work out your friends' names too!

A – Aurora	N – Nia
B – Bea	O – Olivia
C – Caitlin	P – Poppy
D – Darcy	Q – Qiana
E – Eve	R – Rae
F – Fifi	S – Sapphire
G – Grace	T – Tia
H – Heather	U – Ursula
I – Isabella	V – Veronica
J – Jade	W – Willow
K – Katrina	X – Xanthia
L – Leona	Y – Yvette
M – Matilda	Z – Zsa Zsa

My Princess name is...

Leona

polly pocket™ FASHION FUN!

Test your fashion knowledge! Look carefully at the questions Polly's friends are asking, then colour in a heart next to each correct picture.

Which outfit would Polly wear to go shopping?

Lila

a.

b.

c.

Which essential accessory would Polly need on a sunny day?

shani

a.

b.

c.

Which shoes would Polly wear to go running?

crissy

a.

b.

c.

Be creative and design some fashiontastic new patterns on Polly!

How would Polly stay in touch with her friends?

a.

b.

c.

Kerstie

Sparkle World DESIGN

Fashion

Style

Fun

Look for the hidden bangles! Tick the box when you find them! ✓

Lila-C, Shani-A, Crissy-C, Kerstie-B.

SPOT THE DIFFERENCE

Look carefully at the two pictures below. Can you find 7 differences between them? Colour the hearts on picture B as you find each one.

How many pink flowers can you count on these pages?

10

Write the number in the box.

A

my LITTLE PONY

Which cupcake is the odd one out?
Draw a circle around it.

B

1
2
3
4
5
6
7

YooHoo & Friends

Colouring Fun!

Who is YooHoo drawing?
Colour the flower shape next to the right one.

Colour in the big picture of YooHoo and his friends, using the small one to help you.

How many pencils can you count?

7

Write the answer in the box.

A Dream Come True!

Read the story. When you see a picture, say the word.

It was the day of the Big Fashion Show at the Puppy Fashion Academy.  and her friend,  got there early. As soon as the  opened they dashed inside. "I love fashion shows!" giggled , as they waited for it to start. "Me too!" grinned . "I've always dreamed of being a fashion model. Watch this!"  held her head high and began strolling up and down just like a model. At that moment, , the organiser came running up to . "Wow, you're really good at that!" cried . "One of our models has a cold and I'd like you to take her place in the show!"

"Who, me?" squealed , thrilled. "I'd love to!"

Greta

Stella

door

Tiny

 took  backstage and gave her

a gorgeous dress to wear. Then the stylist

added a , and . "Perfect!" declared

. A moment later, the music began! was

on next! She strutted on to the stage holding up her .

Then did a twirl and strutted back again.

The crowd cheered for her!

"You saved the show," grinned

, afterwards. "And

my dream came true at

the same time!" smiled

happily.

HOORAY!

Scruff

handbag

sunglasses

bracelet

Colouring Code!

Colour the picture of Sugar Sprinkles and Sunil! Complete the sums and match your answer to the colour key to find out which colour to use. Colour the rest of the picture any colours you like!

8-6

10+6

4x2

10-8

7x2

8+8

3+1

7-5

Code: 2   4   6   8

Help Blythe find the cupcake that doesn't match the others. Draw a circle around the odd one out.

Sparkle world COLOUR

4+4

5+1

6+4

10-2

6×2

How many hearts?

Write the number in the box.

Tick the box when you find the hidden doughnut. ✓

13-3

10   12   14   16

Stella has hidden some star icons in the butterfly maze. Using your finger, or a pencil, help Aisha collect all of the stars and return them to Stella.

How many stars did you collect?

Write the number in the box.

Sparkle World maze

Stella

Finish

Tecna has placed 10 diamond shapes on these pages. Draw a circle around each one as you find them!

Berry Best Friends Quiz!

Sit opposite your friend with the Sparkle World Annual between you. With a pencil, answer the questions by colouring the heart by your answer. Turn the Annual around and count how many answers your friend got right. Then check your friendship score.

My friend's favourite colour is...

My friend's favourite fruit is...

Her favourite thing to do is...

reading   shopping   dancing

Which animal does she prefer?

cute
kittens   perfect
pups

The thing we most love
to do together is...

 cinema   sleepovers   gossip

cinema   sleepovers   gossip

The thing we most love to do together is....

cute kittens

perfect pups

Which animal does she prefer?

dancing   shopping   reading

Her favourite thing to do is....

My friend's favourite fruit is....

My friend's favourite colour is....

Your friendship score!

0-2

Being super best friends takes time! Don't give up and spend more time together.

Tip: Share two secrets each!

3-4

You are both very good friends, but you have other friends too! You get on great together.

Tip: Bake some cupcakes together!

5

You two are the bestest of friends! BFFs forever! You know everything about each other.

Tip: Make each other a present!

Sparkle World craft

Let's make a sparkletastic... JEWELLERY BOX!

To make the box:

1
Fold an A2 sheet of card in half and draw a grid of 6 equal size squares (14cm x 14cm) in two rows of three.

The fold!

2
Use a ruler to draw the triangular shapes at each end, then cut the card as shown by the dotted lines on the diagram.

Do not cut!

Cut!

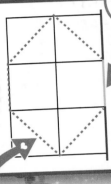

3
Open the card out and place it on a flat surface to score the blue lines and cut the red dotted lines (shown on the diagram).

Cut!

The fold

Score!

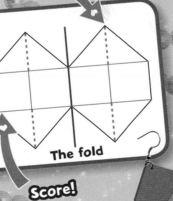

4
Fold the card into a box shape and use glue or tape to fix the triangles that overlap together.

Stick!

To make the trays:

1
Cut a square piece of card 26cm x 26cm. Measure and mark 6.5cm in from each corner and join the lines as shown in blue on the diagram. Carefully cut where the red dotted lines are.

Cut!

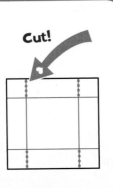

2
Fold the card into a tray shape and glue or stick the overlapping folds to secure it. Then fix with sticky tape inside the jewellery box as shown in the photograph on the opposite page.

Stick!

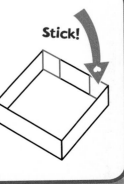

To decorate the jewellery box, we stuck coloured heart and star gems around the outside edges.

Turn to page 74 to make some fabulous, edible jewellery!

coloured gems

Use the butterfly handles to open your jewellery box. We stuck small silk flowers on the trays inside the box. So cute!

patterned paper

butterfly handles

Sparkletastic!

© 2013 Redan

silk flowers

Playtime for Polly!

Colour in Polly using the small picture to help you.

Sparkle World COLOUR

Draw a circle around the **smallest** ball.

POLLY

How many tennis balls?
Don't forget the one on Polly's head!

12

Write the correct number in the box.

Goblin Princess®

The Secret Garden

Matty had a secret. She had planted her own garden in the Goblin castle grounds, and would sneak off every morning to look after it. Goblins aren't supposed to like pretty things. They like to grow weeds instead of flowers. But Matty wasn't like other goblins. She loved flowers.

At breakfast one morning, the queen was reading her favourite gardening magazine. "Our weedbeds aren't nearly overgrown enough," she told the king. The king agreed. "I've spotted some awful flowers growing too," he grumbled. "They need to be ripped out."

My secret garden!

Mr Dollop, the gardener, arrived later that day. "I want poison ivy and jumbo thorns," the queen told him. "And there are some disgusting flowers in the corner that need to be ripped out before they spread."

"Oh no! When Mr Dollop finds my secret garden, he'll tear it out," Matty told Smoky. "My pretty flower garden will be destroyed and all our hard work will be ruined. I don't think there's anything we can do about it."

Mr Dollop had a lot of work to do. The queen wanted lots of new weeds to be planted, and the hedges trimmed into scary shapes. But before he started all that, Mr Dollop needed to get rid of all the pesky flowers.

These flowers are choking all the weeds!

Here's a mug of hot mud.

As Mr Dollop took a break, Matty tip-toed over to her secret garden. It was ruined.

It's all gone!

Matty looked down, and noticed something inside a hollow log on the ground. Inside, were some beautiful flowers. It was a perfect, tiny little secret garden.

Some of my seeds must have blown in here!

The king and queen were so pleased with their new garden. "I just heard that 'Ghastly Gardens' magazine want to put our garden on their cover," the queen cooed. Matty was pleased with her garden too. "It might be tiny, but it's all mine," Matty said to Smoky. "And it's our secret!"

Pony Trail Puzzle!

Start

How many orange butterflies can you count on these pages?

Write the number in the box.

Help Rainbow Dash find her way through the shape trail to Twilight Sparkle. You can only move to the next space if it is the same shape or colour. You can move up, down, left or right through the maze to the finish.

Can you find the frog? Draw a circle around it when you do!

Finish

Fab Fashion Finding Game!

Guess Who!
Colour the star next to the friend
that matches all the clues below.
1. I wear a dress.
2. I don't have glasses.
3. I love pretty bows.

Let's make some fabulous...
Fruit Sushi!

Ask an adult to help you cut the fruit!

Super Strawberries

Carefully slice the ends off a large strawberry, then add pieces of kiwi fruit on top.

You will need:
two big bananas
some large strawberries
fruit strings
some chocolate coconut bars
and some additional fruit –
we used kiwi and melon.

Banana Rolls

Chop a banana into thick blocks and wrap a fruit string around them. Top with slices of different fruit.

© 2013 Redan

Bite-size Bananas

Slice a banana into thin strips and lay flat. Place some other pieces of fruit on top.

Cute Coconut

Cut the chocolate off a coconut bar then top with thinly sliced fruit. Yummy!

Melon Wedges

Slice some melon into thick wedge shapes then finish by wrapping some fruit string around it.

If you don't like coconut, mix up a bowl of rice crispies with a little syrup instead!

nickelodeon

Winx CLUB

Word Puzzle!

Sparkle World PUZZLE

Write a letter in each shape
to make two words.

sta (r) ainbow

belie (f) riends

crysta (l) olly

banan (a) rtist

disc (o) cean

Answer: Flora

Flora

Bloom

Unscramble the letters in the flower shapes
to reveal the name of one of the Winx fairies.
Write your answer in the blue flower shapes.

Tick the box
when you find
the flower.

How many?

Write the number
in the box.

© 2013 Rainbow S.r.l. and Viacom International Inc.

THE GOLDEN LION

Read the story.
When you see a picture,
say the word instead.

YOOHOO

YOOTOPEDIA

LION

 and his friends were

trekking across the African desert.

"The  says the world's biggest

golden lives here," said .

"Ooh, I want to meet the biggest !"

cried , excitedly. "Let's find him!" The

friends searched and searched but there was no

sign of the 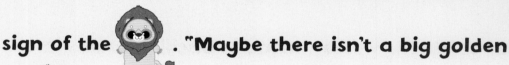 . "Maybe there isn't a big golden

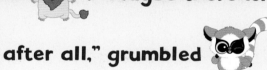 after all," grumbled . "The

was wrong!" Just then, spotted a very odd

looking with a red mane. "Hello," said .

"Have you seen a big golden ?" "I used to be

the big golden ," sighed the . "Some

red fruit fell on me and turned my mane red!

Now the other animals keep laughing at me!"

 looked in the 📖 to see if there was anything that might help the sad 🦁.

"Aha!" said 🐒. "It says there's a special stream on that 🪨 ahead of us! That might help!" They all climbed to the top of the 🪨, and the 🦁 splashed the water on his mane. Everyone gasped as it turned from red to gold! "My golden mane is back!" shouted the 🦁, happily. "Hurray!" everyone cheered.

"The 📖 was right after all!" chuckled 🐿️.

"The world's biggest golden 🦁 does live here!"

HURRAY!

ROODEE

CHEWOO

LEMMEE

PAMMEE

ROCK

Best Friends BINGO!

You will need:
2-4 friends, a pencil and 2 dice.
How to play:
Each player chooses a character and takes it in turns to roll the dice. Add up the total and check which picture matches the number thrown. Whoever has that picture in their circle should cross it out. The winner is the first player to cross out all 6 of their pictures and shout "BINGO!"

How many?
Write the answer in the box.

Sparkle World game

Pepper

Vinnie

My Little Pony™

FRIENDS FOREVER

Pinkie Pie

n

w

g

Answer: The hidden word is wings.

Colour in Pinkie Pie and Rainbow Dash, using the small pictures to help you.

Sparkle World colour

Rainbow Dash

How many yellow hearts can you count on these pages?

Write the number in the box.

There are 5 letters hidden in this picture. Rearrange them to spell out the secret word.

Clue: Rainbow Dash has these!

Polly's Party Balloon Puzzle!

Are the numbers you follow on the trail odd or even?

☐ odd   ☐ even

Tick the correct box.

Polly

Polly's spell has created too many party balloons! Help her find a way across to Phoebe the Fashion Fairy. With your finger, or a pencil, follow the numbers in the correct order from 2 to 66. The number sequence goes up in twos.

Sparkle World PUZZLE

32 59 62 66 Finish
60 61 64
34 58
35
36 56
38
54
40 50
52
51 48
44
42 46
41

Phoebe

YooHoo & FRIENDS™

© Aurora World Corp.

YooHoo Animal Howlers!

Sparkle World JOKES

What's tall, yellow and smells nice?
A Giraffodil!

What goes OOM, OOM?
A cow walking backwards!

What time do ducks get up in the morning?
At the quack of dawn!

What do cats eat for breakfast?
Mewslie!

What's a horses favourite game?
Stable Tennis!

How do sick pigs get to the hospital?
In a hambulance!

Which fish sleep a lot?
Kippers!

What do whales eat?
Fish and ships!

What kind of ape talks a lot?
A Blaboon!

What do you call a monkey who loves chips?
A chip-monk!

What goes squeak-bang, squeak-bang?
Dynamice!

Bad Hair Day!

1. At the Littlest Pet Shop, Mrs Twombly was in a panic. "Oh dear me!" she cried. "What's wrong?" asked Blythe. Our head dog groomer is off work poorly today and I have clients in soon!" "I can do it, Mrs Twombly!" said Blythe.

2. "Do you have any experience?" asked Mrs Twombly, "Well, um, yes! I have lots of experience in making things look pretty," explained Blythe. "Okay then!" smiled Mrs Twombly, who brought Zoe the spaniel over to Blythe.

3. "Do you have any experience in dog grooming, Blythe?" asked a curious Zoe. "Of course I do!" Blythe giggled. Blythe was so distracted chatting away to Zoe that she didn't realise how much hair she was cutting off.

4. When Blythe finally looked down at her handiwork on Zoe, her face froze with horror. She had cut far too much hair off Zoe who was covered in uneven patches! "So, how do I look?" yapped an excitable Zoe.

5. Blythe started to sweep up the hair. "Erm, you look really great, Zoe!" enthused a panicked Blythe. "That's fabulous!" sighed a relieved Zoe. "I'm being entered into a competition this afternoon, so I need to look my best!"

6. "Please can I see myself in the mirror, Blythe?" asked Zoe. "Erm..I'm not sure where they are kept I'm afraid," stuttered Blythe. "Ah, here's one!" Zoe found a mirror and held it up to her face. "NOOO! I'm ruined!" she cried.

7. Just as Blythe started to apologise to Zoe, Mrs Twombly came in to check how they were getting on. Blythe wrapped Zoe in a towel and placed cucumber slices on her eyes to hide her. "All fine in here thanks!" laughed Blythe.

8. After Mrs Twombly left, Blythe apologised to Zoe and explained she got so carried away cutting her hair and chatting to her, that she hadn't realised how short it was. " me try combing it," suggested Blythe, but it didn't work

9. "Blythe, Zoe's owners are here to collect her," called Mrs Twombly. "Oh, no!" cried Blythe. "I will have to tell them the truth!" "Don't worry, Blythe!" reassured Zoe, "It was just an accident." Blythe hid Zoe behind her back.

10. Once Blythe reached the counter, she took a deep breath. "Hmm, where do I start.." Whilst Blythe tried to think of what to say, Minka sneaked up behind her with some glue and purple fluff and started to fix Zoe's coat.

11. "Come on, Blythe! Hand Zoe over to Clarissa!" instructed Mrs Twombly. "I'm..sorry," sighed Blythe, as she produced Zoe from behind her back who looked perfect and sparkly! "What are you sorry for Blythe? Our princess looks amazing!" cheered Clarissa. Zoe looked perfect. "Oh..Yes! She's beautiful!" smiled Blythe, as she spotted Minka run away. "Blythe, you must help with grooming again!" said an excitable Mrs Twombly. "Hmm, maybe one day!" giggled Blythe giving Zoe a wink.

It's All About ME!

Turn these pages into your very own 'about me' profile. Fill in all of the gaps and stick photos in the special spaces! Have fun!

About Me

Name: ....Lucia........................

Birthday: 18th Febuwery

Home town: ....44.............

Stick a picture of you here!

My lucky number!

8

Write the number in the box.

Tick your favourite pet?

dog ✓   cat ☐

My top foods!

1. ...chips......
2. cicken......
3. cheese......
4. ham......
5. carruts......

My favourite band:

one Direction

My favourite song:

let it go

Cut and stick your favourite pictures!

Sparkle World Design

Stick your picture here!

My Family!

Stick your picture here!

My Favourite Day!

Stick your picture here!

My BFF!

My BFF is
Lowies

My favourite subject at school is:

irish

A+

Circle the words that best describe you.

I am...
happy
friendly
fashionable
loud
honest
quiet
fun

Colour the flower your favourite colour!

Which do you prefer? Tick the box!

✓ **Summer**

Winter

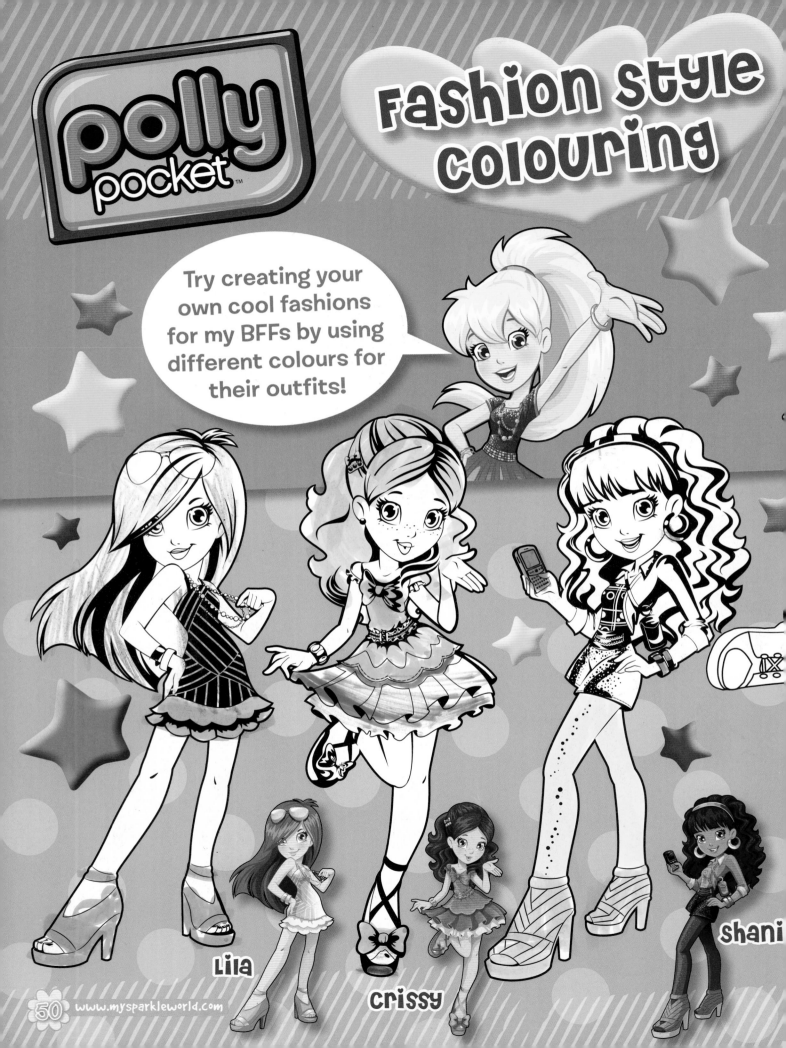

Colour in the pictures of Polly and her BFFs using the small pictures to help you.

Sparkle World COLOUR

kerstie

polly

What's your favourite fashion essential?

www.mysparkleworld.com 51

TAIL CHASE RACE!

You will need:

A dice, counters and 1 to 3 friends to play with.

How to play:

Choose who each player will be and place the counters on the start squares. Take it in turns to roll the dice and move the number of spaces shown. When you land on a picture square, follow its instruction. The first player to make their way around the board and up the path to their finish wins!

Daniel Player 1

Gigi finish

Gigi start

Da... sta...

Gigi Player 3

How many of Zoey's bones can you count on these pages?

Write the answer in the box.

11

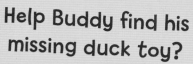

Help Buddy find his missing duck toy?

Tick the box when you find it.

✓

Peanut Player 2

Peanut start

Peanut finish

aniel finish

noop finish

Snoop start

Snoop Player 4

If you land on:

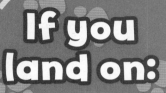

Frisbee
Move forward 2 spaces and bark like a dog!

Ball
Move back 1 space and roll over!

Apple
Miss a go and tickle your tummy!

Littlest Pets Portrait!

Sparkle World COLOUR

Help Blythe finish her portrait of Buttercream Sunday by using a pencil to join the dots, starting at the number 1.

Remember to colour me in!

How many?

Write the answer in the box.

1. It was the day before the Baking Contest in Berry Bitty City. "Hi, Blueberry! I'm entering the baking contest and I want a new recipe," explained Strawberry Shortcake. "Can I see some of your recipe books?" "Yes, here are some lovely ones," smiled Blueberry, bringing out a couple of recipe books. "This one looks perfect!" said Strawberry. "I'll take it!"

2. A moment later, Lemon Meringue arrived. "I want the very newest recipe book, please," she asked. "But we have lots of other ones too," suggested Blueberry. "No, I really must have the newest," insisted Lemon.

3. Soon after that, Orange Blossom came along. "I'd like the Berry Bitty Baking Book, please," said Orange. "But you might like one of these better," said Blueberry. "No, I've made my mind up" said Orange.

4. Blueberry was bursting to know what recipes the three girls had chosen! Later that day, she was picking some berries when she spotted Strawberry, Lemon and Orange out gathering some fruit for their recipes. "Hey, Strawberry, what are you planning to bake for the contest?" asked Lemon. "It's a secret new recipe," smiled Strawberry. "So is mine!" laughed Lemon. "And mine!" giggled Orange. Blueberry sighed. She still had no idea what they were going to bake!

5. Soon after that, the air was filled with the delicious smell of baking. "Mmm! I wonder what they're baking?" Blueberry asked Plum Pudding, Cherry Jam and Raspberry Torte. "That's what we were wondering!" said Plum.

6. The next day, Princess Berrykin arrived in town to judge the Baking Contest. It was almost time for the contest to begin! At last everyone would find out what Strawberry, Lemon and Orange had been baking!

7. Everyone gasped when they saw the cakes. All the girls had all baked exactly the same cupcakes! "They're all berry delicious!" chuckled Princess Berrykin. "You'll just have to share first prize!"

8. "Oh, muffin crumbs! I guessed this might happen!" cried Blueberry. "Everyone bought the same recipe books even though I tried to stop you. And then you all chose the same cupcake recipe too! It's a disaster!"

9. "No, it isn't!" smiled Strawberry. "We all had berry great fun baking them and that's what really matters." "Yes and the good thing is they all turned out perfectly!" nodded Orange, happily. "That means there are enough berrylicious prize-winning cupcakes for everyone to try!" giggled Lemon. "Anyone for a cupcake?" "Me, me!" everyone shouted. Blueberry smiled as everyone shared the cupcakes. It was a sweeter than sweet ending after all!

YooHoo & FRIENDS™

© Aurora World Corp.

HOO ARE YOO?

Mostly pink

You are a great listener and a caring and sensitive friend to everyone. You love to explore nature, visit new places and meet new people, just like Pammee!

Mostly yellow

You are often the centre of attention, fun, outgoing and sporty in your nature. You like to push your yourself to your limits and get stuck into new experiences, just like Chewoo!

Colour in the flower next to the five pictures that you are most drawn to, then count which colour you have the most of. This will reveal which YooHoo character you are most like!

How many?

Write the answer in the box.

Mostly green

You are positive and confident in everything you do. You especially love to spend time with friends. You like to go on exciting adventures to discover new places, just like YooHoo!

Mostly blue

You are a thoughtful and caring person. Sometimes you like to chill out on your own, learning new things to share with your friends, just like Lemmee!

Mostly purple

You are artistic, creative and friendly. You are an excellent problem solver, who loves reading books and writing stories, just like Roodee!

Answer: 5 Butterflies.

Sparkle World craft

Let's have a... POP STAR Party!

A Parent and Child Activity

Star Topped Pizza

Carefully cut star shapes out of cheese slices and place on top of some mini pizzas to create some fabulous star topped pizza treats.

Invites

Why not use a CD case for your invite. Download the design we made at www.mysparkleworld.com or make your own cover to invite your friends to your party! Remember to include the date, time, place and a contact number for you on them.

You could decorate it with glitter and shiny star shapes.

Name Tags

Design a VIP name tag for each of your guests, so they can feel really special!

You can buy these lanyards online or use a hole punch in the top of your name tag design and thread some funky coloured string through it.

Use some blank CDs for your drink coasters.

Rachel
POP STAR Party!

Don't forget to thank your friends for coming!

Thank you for coming to my... POP STAR Party!

To download these designs, go to: www.mysparkleworld.com

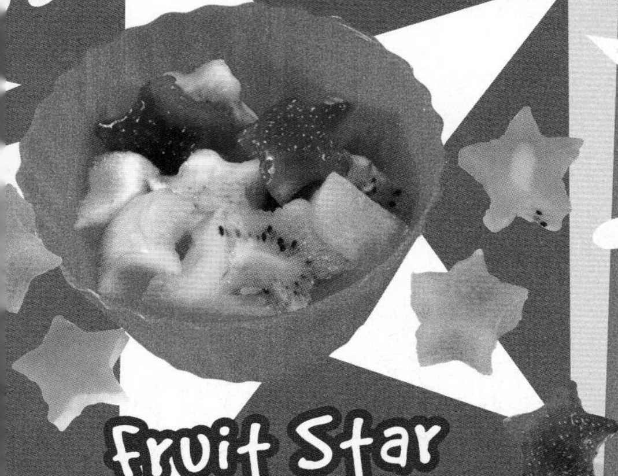

Fruit Star Dessert

Use a star-shaped cookie cutter to press shapes out of thickly sliced fruit and serve as a tasty dessert.

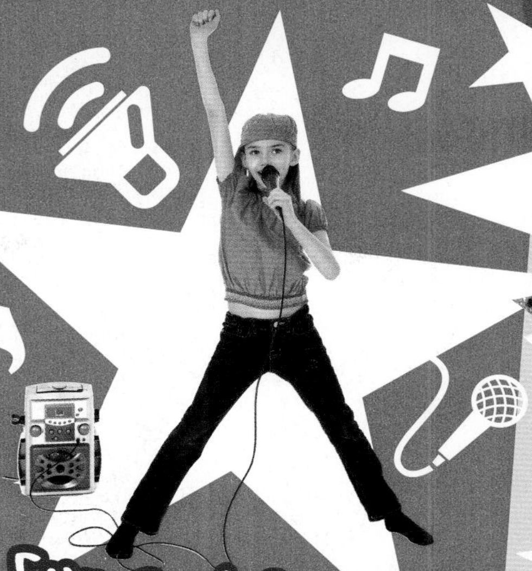

Fun and Games

Have some karaoke fun!

Play 'Pop Star Says!'
(Simon says)

Get dressed up for a red carpet photo shoot!

Play musical statues.

Treat time

Zoe
Rachel
POP

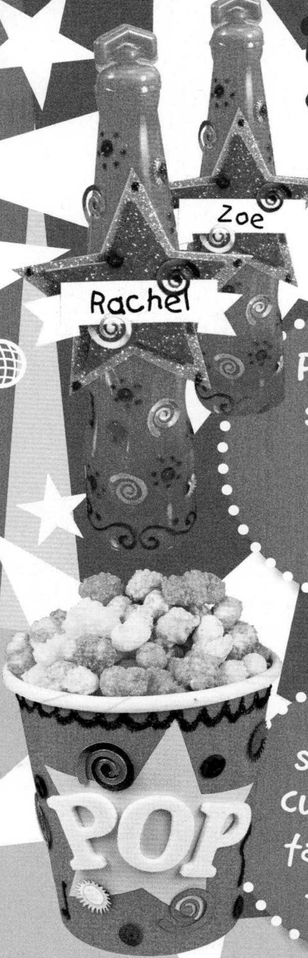

Personalise soft drink bottles for your guests.

Decorate some plastic cups for your take-away treats

Rachel
Zoe
Kim
Carrie
POP
POP
Rock n Roll

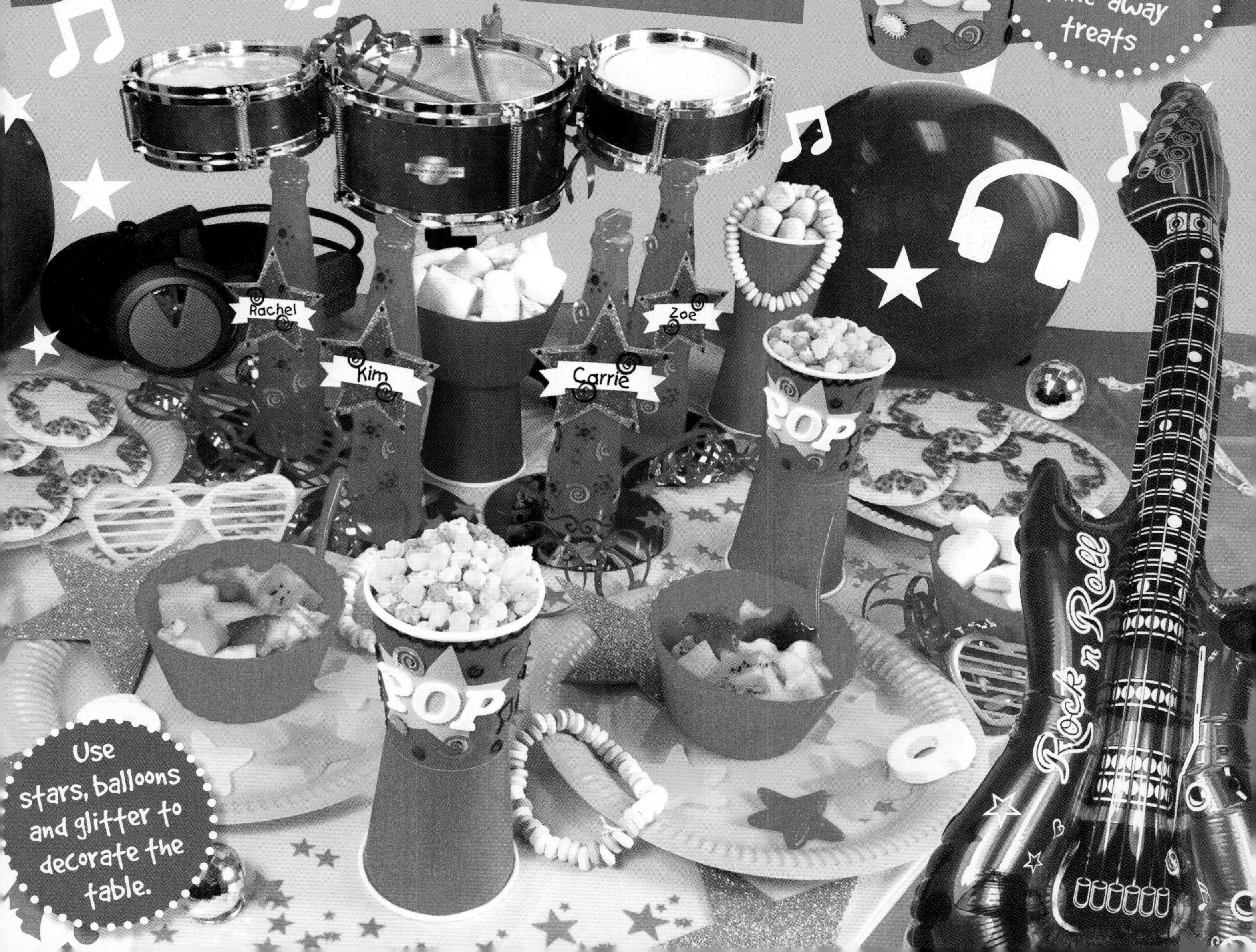

Use stars, balloons and glitter to decorate the table.

PUPPIES IN PERIL!

Using your finger, or a pencil, help Brandy rescue the puppies from the maze! Colour in the paw print next to each one as you find them.

n

e

b

START

Brandy

Some of the heart shapes in the maze contain a letter. Write the matching coloured letters in the correct circles to reveal Georgie's favourite treat.

How many?
Write the answers in the boxes.

Dot

Bandit

Clarissa

Sammy

YOU DID IT!!

FINISH

Georgie loves...

b o n e s

Which 2 colours make green?
Shade in the stars with the correct colours.

Sparkle World colour

Colour answer: Yellow and blue make green.

How many?

✓ purple flowers

✓ raindrops

✓ stars

Write the answer in each box.

Colour the star in your favourite colour!

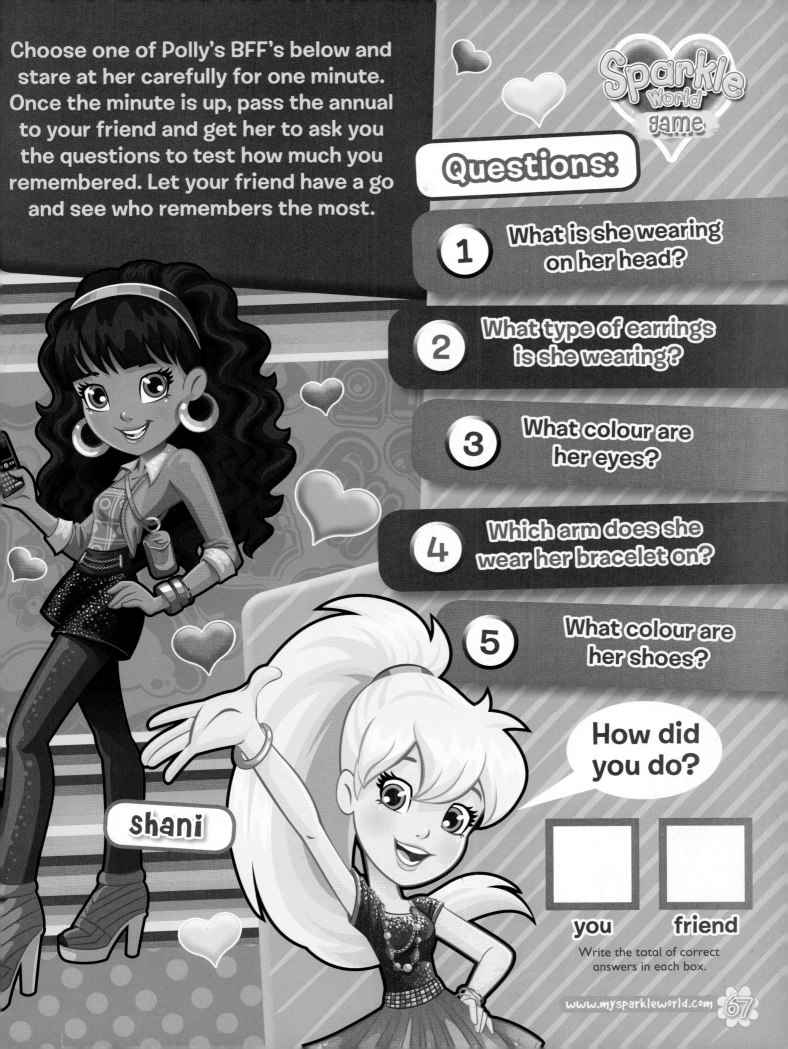

YooHoo & FRIENDS™

© Aurora World Corp.

Learn to Draw YooHoo!

Follow the simple steps below to draw YooHoo!

1. Start by drawing a group of circles to make the body.

2. Draw more circles for the face, hands and feet. Add a wavy tail shape.

3. Finish by drawing in the details on the face and tail.

Try drawing YooHoo's friends in the same way!

Use this space
to try drawing
YooHoo yourself!

Sparkle World
DRAW

**Which are
there more of?**

Tick the box next
to the correct one.

butterflies ✓ ladybirds ✓

Fairy Fun Board Game!

You will need: A dice and a counter for each player.
How to play: Take it in turns to roll the dice and move forward the number of spaces shown. Follow the instructions on the square your turn ends on. The winner is the first person to reach the finish!

41

42 Flutter down to 37

43

44

45 Roll again!

40

39

38

37

36 Fly down to 24

21

22

23 Fly up to 38

24

25

20 Roll again!

19 Slide down to 3

18

17

16 Float down to 6

START

1

2

3 Miss a go!

4 Fly up to 17

5

Colour in Stella's stars to complete the pattern!

Puppytastic WORDSEARCH!

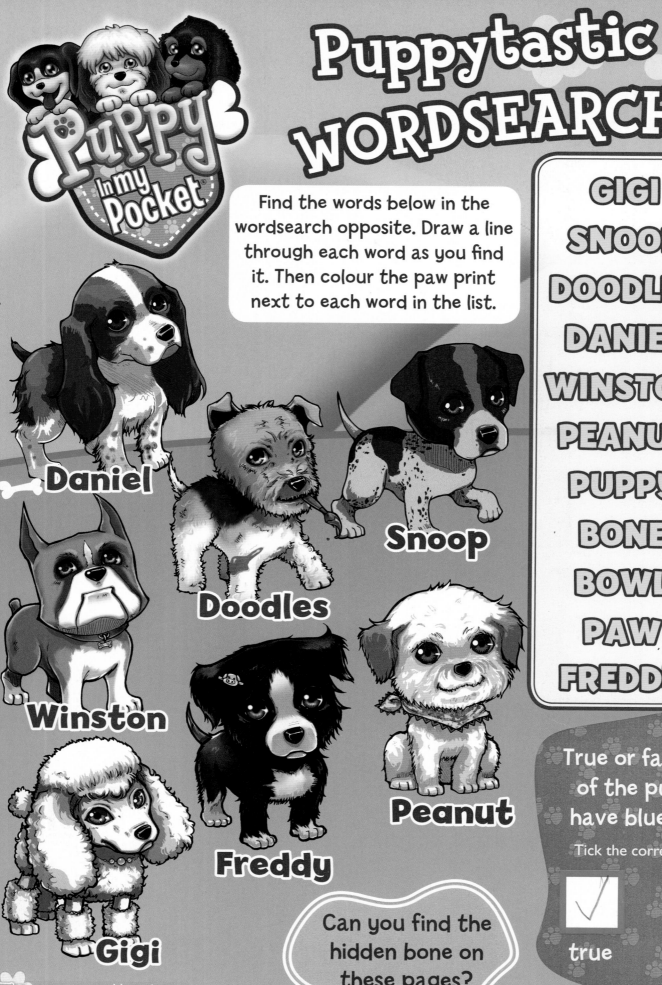

Find the words below in the wordsearch opposite. Draw a line through each word as you find it. Then colour the paw print next to each word in the list.

GIGI
SNOOP
DOODLES
DANIEL
WINSTON
PEANUT
PUPPY
BONE
BOWL
PAW
FREDDY

Daniel

Snoop

Doodles

Winston

Freddy

Peanut

Gigi

Can you find the hidden bone on these pages?

True or false, two of the puppies have blue eyes?

Tick the correct box.

✓ true

false

How many dogs are wearing something around their neck?

3

Write the number in the box.

How many dogs are raising one paw?

1

Write the number in the box.

Sparkle World
wordsearch

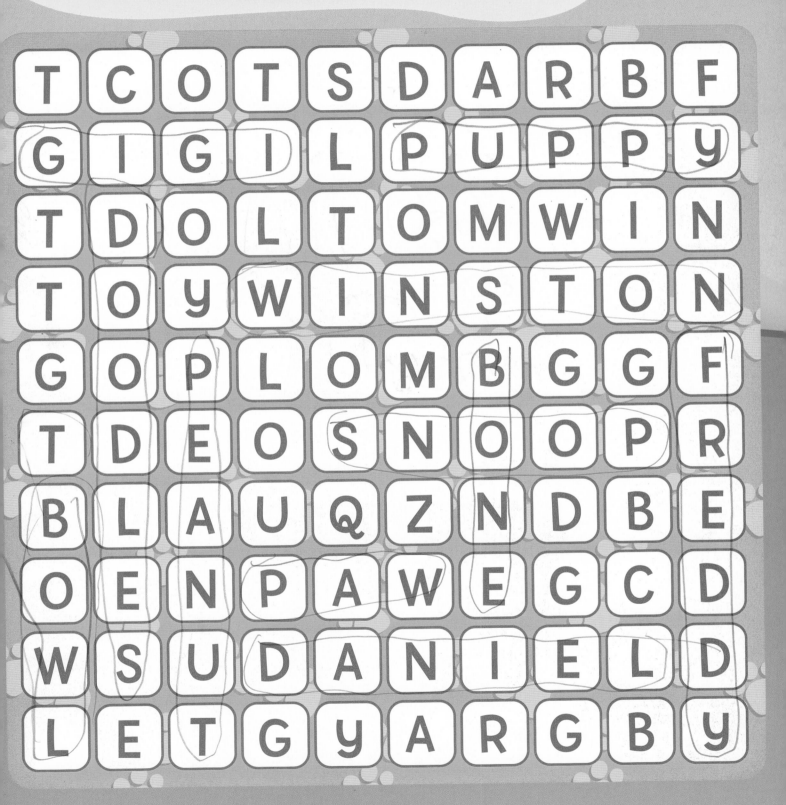

T C O T S D A R B F
G I G I L L P U P P Y
T D O L T O M W I N
T O Y W I N S T O N N
G O P L O M B G G F
T D E O S N O O P R
B L A U Q Z N D B E
O E N P A W E G C D
W S U D A N I E L D
L E T G Y A R G B Y

Sparkle World craft

Let's make some... Edible Necklaces!

Why not make this tasty treat necklace for yourself or your BFF?

A Parent and Child Activity

tube shapes

round shapes

You will need:
Ready to roll icing, food colouring, thin ribbon and a cocktail stick.

split colour beads

diamond shapes

letter beads (using an icing pen)

z o e

1
Split the ready to roll icing into even amounts and add a few drops of food colouring. Knead each block until it is evenly coloured.

2
Roll out different shapes for the beads, then carefully push a cocktail stick through each one to make a hole. Ask an adult to help you with this part as cocktail sticks are very sharp!

3
Carefully cut the ribbon to the length you want for your necklace, then thread the icing shapes on to it to make your funky, edible jewellery!

Top Tip
Try adding some vanilla or mint essence when mixing the colours to add flavour to the icing.

Top Tip
Cut the ribbon shorter, to fit your wrist, and make a matching bracelet!

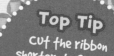

My Little Pony

The Scary Campout!

1. Sweetie Belle, Apple Bloom and Scootaloo were camping out for the night. "Now, are you sure you little fillies won't be scared?" asked Applejack. "Who us?" grinned her little sister, Apple Bloom. "Ha! We're not scared of the dark!" "Well don't tell any scary stories, just in case!" smiled Applejack.

2. "Huh! Scary stories don't worry me!" giggled Scootaloo, as soon as Applejack had gone. "Want to hear one?" The ponies nodded! As it grew darker, Scootaloo told her friends a hair-raising story about a hungry dragon that lived in the forest.

3. Suddenly, Sweetie Belle heard a rustling noise. "Shh! Did you hear that?" she whispered. "It was probably just the wind," said Apple Bloom. A moment later, something dark with enormous wings fluttered overhead. "Th-that wasn't the wind!" squeaked Sweetie Belle. "I think it was... the hungry dragon!"

4. "Aaaaah!" shrieked the three ponies, running through the town streets. "Help! Help!" "What's the matter?" asked Twilight Sparkle, looking out from the library balcony. "Help us, Twilight Sparkle!" yelled Scootaloo. "The hungry dragon is after us!"

5. "That's not a dragon," chuckled Twilight Sparkle. "It's Princess Luna! It's her duty to guard the night." "That's right," smiled Princess Luna, fluttering down. "I'm sorry if I scared you. I was just keeping an eye on you all. Come along, I'll see you safely back to your tent."

6. "Phew!" said Sweetie Belle as they followed the Princess. "I'm so glad it wasn't the hungry dragon." "Me too!" grinned Apple Bloom. "But maybe Applejack was right. Let's not tell any more scary stories, okay?" "Okay!" giggled the ponies.

polly pocket™

Friendship Quiz!

Polly wants to find out what kind of friend you are. Do this fun quiz to find out! Get your friends to do it too!

Do you like taking lots of photographs?

Do you love painting and drawing?

Do you love singing and performing?

Are you good at sharing treats with your friends?

Is it important to keep up to date with the latest fashions?

Have you ever customised some of your clothes?

Are you good at listening and keeping secrets?

Kerstie

You are creative and fashion conscious! You love dancing and entertaining your friends. It is important to you that your friends are always smiling. Your friends think you are fab! You love painting, drawing and creating!

Crissy

You are great fun and give your friends the best advice. You are trustworthy which is why your friends feel they can tell you all their secrets! You love problem solving and you always help friends who are in a sticky situation!

Start!

Do you like to chat for hours on the phone?

Key:
Y = yes
N = no

Sparkle World QUIZ

Do you prefer to go to parties than staying in to watch a film?

Are you the joker in your group of friends?

Do you like having sleepovers with your friends?

Are you happiest when you are playing outdoors?

Do you like to look after animals?

Are you an organised person?

Do you like to give presents as well as receive them?

Do you prefer activity holidays to chilled out beach breaks?

Shani

You are a fun friend! You love to make up games and plan parties. You are at your happiest when you are planning a day out shopping, partying or having a sleepover. Your friends rely on you to be the organiser of the group! Your friends love your fun nature!

Lila

You are the chilled out friend who loves the outdoors. You love to go on adventures and spend lots of time outside. You are the explorer of the group and you are fearless! Your friends love your adventurous side. There is never a dull moment!

Blythe's Checklist!

Sparkle World
COLOUR

Zoe

© 2013 Hasbro. All Rights Reserved.

Fairy Destiny

The Winx fairies will help you discover what to do with your future! How to play: Stare at each of the circles that contain a Winx fairy for 30 seconds. Close your eyes. When you open them again, the fairy that jumps out at you first will reveal their suggestion.

Musa

You are a deep thinker like Musa. You love to use your imagination. Start making a scrapbook or keeping a dream diary to record all of your thoughts, hopes, memories and dreams for the future.

Aisha

You are a happy, playful person like Aisha! You are excellent at making up games for you and your friends as you have an amazing imagination! You always play fair. Why not play a board game now?

Stella

Like Stella, you are a brilliant problem solver. You use your head as well as your heart when making important life decisions. Your friends love how well balanced you are as a friend. Why not invite a friend to tea?

Bloom

You love singing and dancing like Bloom. You love learning new dance routines and songs. Your friends think you are extremely loyal and you will always stand up for what is right. You are also very kind.

Tecna

Like Tecna, you love nothing more than to travel to new places. You have a strong sense of adventure and love to make lots of memories! Why not suggest to a friend to go on a local farm walk or along a forest trial?

Flora

Like Flora, you are creative and girly. You love pampering sessions and making things for friends and family. You are excellent at choosing colours for clothing. Why not try and design your own fashion range?

Read the story. When you see a picture, say the word instead.

 wanted a cute photo of her pets to share with her friends.

 set up the camera for a ten second delay, while [Polly] lined up her

[cat] , [dog] , [birds] and [bunny] . "Everybody ready?" said [Polly] ,

standing back. But before [Lea] could take the photo, the [dog]

and [cat] started charging around the room, the [bunny] hopped after

them and the [birds] started flying about, chirping loudly! "Hey,

come back!" cried [Polly] and [Lea] , chasing after the pets. [Polly] just

managed to catch the [bunny] but she quickly wriggled out of her arms.

Then [Lea] tried to grab the [birds] , but missed and landed face first

on the bed. "This isn't working!" sighed [Polly] , dropping to the floor.

polly

cat

bunny

Sparkle World story

kerstie

dog

birds

"I give up," wailed , flopping down beside her. Suddenly the ,

 and  came dashing up and pounced on  and ,

wanting to play. As the  swooped down to join in the fun,

one of them tapped her claw on the camera shutter button. "Quick,

smile!" cried . "We've got ten seconds before it goes off!"

CLICK! The camera flashed!  and  rushed to the camera to

look at the photo. "Wow! Best pet photo ever!"

gasped . "Of course, that's

just how I planned it all along,"

grinned . "Well... sort of!"

Strawberry Shortcake™

Super Sweet Colouring!

Complete the colour pattern.

Colour the picture of Strawberry Shortcake, Orange Blossom, Plum Pudding and the Berrykins, using the small picture to help you.

How many Berrykins can you find on these pages?

Write the number in the box.

Winx CLUB

Puzzle Time!
Have fun working out these Winx Puzzles!

1 Tecna

2.

1.

4.

3.

Colour in the diamond next to the shadow shape that exactly matches Tecna.

Stella

2

How many butterflies?

9

Write the number in the box.

How many stars?

9

Write the number in the box.

How many music notes?

5

Write the number in the box.

Tick the box when you find this flower.

✓

3

Help Bloom solve the puzzle by drawing lines to the space where each piece fits. Colour in the hearts when you match each piece.

Bloom

Colour in the circle next to the odd picture out.

4 The Winx fairies names are hidden somewhere in the wordsearch below. Draw a line through each one as you find them.

```
M U S A A W A N A B A
X G M N I I X I W L W
U O C X C S M R I O I
Z E B O F C H W N O N
T N S T E L L A C M X
O O K F F L O R A S I
```

AISHA
STELLA
MUSA
FLORA
BLOOM
TECNA

5 Find an extra 4 letter word hidden in the wordsearch!

_ _ _ _ X

Write the answer in the box.

Look at the wordsearch and write the pink letters in order, moving across the lines from left to right to reveal Musa's hidden message!

Musa

MAGIC ROCKS!

Aisha

Flora

Read the sentences below and colour in a **T** for true or **F** for false.

7

Bloom's wing pattern features a heart shape.

(T) (F)

Stella's hair is brown.

(T) (F)

6 Finish Flora's sudoku puzzle by drawing the missing icons in the empty spaces. Each one can only appear once in each row or column.

Claudia The Accessories Fairy!

Kirsty and Rachel had designed their own outfits for a fashion competition. Now they needed things to go with them, but everything in the accessory shop seemed dull or broken! Suddenly a tiny fairy flew out of a jewellery display. It was Claudia the Accessories Fairy!

"Jack Frost has stolen my magical necklace!" cried Claudia. "Since he took it, the magic is making all accessories look horrible instead of pretty!" "We'll help look for it," promised Kirsty. They set off to search the shopping centre.

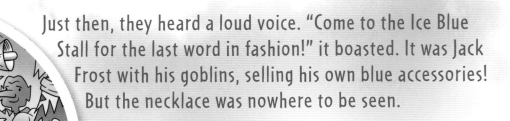

Just then, they heard a loud voice. "Come to the Ice Blue Stall for the last word in fashion!" it boasted. It was Jack Frost with his goblins, selling his own blue accessories! But the necklace was nowhere to be seen.

Claudia waved her wand and the girls turned into fairies. They followed a goblin to a workshop where more goblins were making the accessories. "Look, Claudia!" whispered Rachel. "The goblin supervisor is wearing your necklace!"

At that moment, the supervisor spotted a pair of green gloves. "Everything's got to be blue!" he yelled. "But we like green!" argued a goblin. The other goblins all joined in. The supervisor was so angry he ripped off the magic necklace. "I give up!" he snapped.

At once Claudia darted down and grabbed the necklace. "Jack Frost is going to be so mad," gulped a goblin, as they all ran from the room! "Now I can make the accessories gorgeous again!" smiled Claudia, restoring the girls to normal size. Kirsty and Rachel smiled. They had some shopping to do, starting by choosing some beautiful accessories!